FROM THE F...

THE JOCK OF WELLINGTON—INVENTOR OF THE BOOT THAT WON THE BATTLE OF GEORDIELOO!

WAH!

EEK!

CLAN CHIEF SITTING JOCK—HAS SCALPED MANY GEORDIES, AND SAVED THEM GOING TO THE BARBER!

WOO!

GULP!

THE PIED PIPER OF JOCKLAND—PLAYED SPELLBINDING MUSIC, BUT IT WAS A BIG LET-DOWN TO THE GEORDIES!

SKIRL

LOVER'S LEAP 269 FEET

£2·25

D0726270

Printed and published in Great Britain by D. C. THOMSON & CO., LTD., 185 Fleet Street, London, EC4A 2HS.
© D. C. THOMSON & CO., LTD., 1984.
ISBN 0 85116 296 7

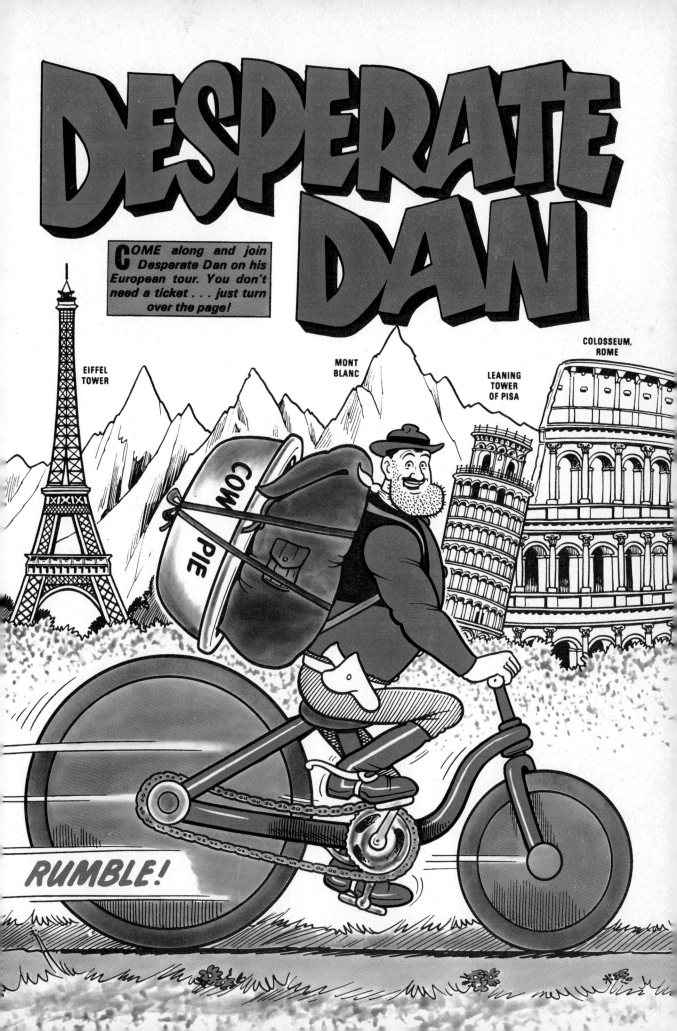

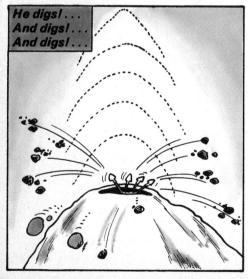

I KNOW WHAT TO GET FOR DAD—AND HE CAN'T RUIN OUR FOOTBALL FUN WITH THIS.

So—

A HAMMOCK! WHY, THANK YOU, SMASHER!

HAMMOCK

I'LL HELP YOU SLING IT BETWEEN THE GARDEN TREES, DAD.

SHOOT, SMASHER!

BIFF!

SNAP!

WHAT ON EARTH!

YOW! OOF!

SNARL! I KNOW WHERE I'LL SLING MY HAMMOCK!

OH, NO! MY GIFT TO DAD HAS SPOILED OUR FOOTBALL FUN AGAIN!

So—

Meanwhile, back at the duckpond—

I'VE MANAGED TO FREE MYSELF, NOW I'LL FREE YOU.

PULL!

THANKS, PAL!

Then, it's along to the Geordies' hut—

THIS IS MY PAL, TWEETER SMYTHE— HE'S AN ELECTRONIC GENIUS!

NEVER MIND THAT, ARNOLD. WE'VE GOT BAD NEWS!

BUZZZZ!

—AND THE JOCKS HAVE GOT THIS BIG HULKING BRUTE WHO KEEPS THROWING HIS WEIGHT AROUND.

THAT'S BAD! WE'D BETTER FETCH ALL OUR WEAPONS!

ER . . . PERHAPS I CAN HELP.

BZZZZ!

YOU?

So—

I HOPE TWEETER KNOWS WHAT HE'S DOING, SENDING US TO COLLECT ALL THESE OLD CAR PARTS.

DESPERATE DAWG

PLENTY OF WINDOWS IN DOGGIE PATCH— OOPS!

CLONK!

OUCH!

I'LL JUST GO AND FILL MY BUCKET AT THE PUMP SO THAT I CAN START MY NEW BUSINESS— WINDOW CLEANING!

ER...SORRY, SHERIFF!

SO YOU SHOULD BE—YOU CLUMSY TWIT!

MY BUCKET'S BADLY BENT! MAYBE I CAN PUNCH IT OUT STRAIGHT AGAIN!

WOW! THERE GOES THE BOTTOM!

CRASH!

CLUNK!

OW!

I'LL JUST HAVE TO GO AND BUY ANOTHER BUCKET!

So—

HARDWARE

WELL I'VE GOT A NICE NEW BUCKET! NOW TO START WORK!

Later—

NO, DAWG! MY WINDOWS DON'T NEED CLEANING!

MY WINDOWS DON'T NEED CLEANING EITHER!

HMM! BUSINESS ISN'T SO LIVELY AFTER ALL!

HOOK

Dawg's ladder catches around a fence plank!

PYOING!

THERE GOES DAWG! I'LL GIVE HIM A TICKING OFF ABOUT HIS CLUMSINESS!

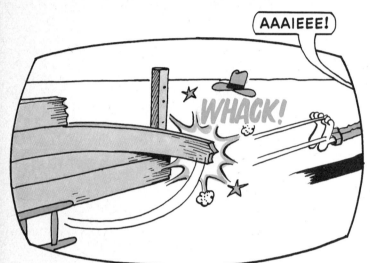

AAAIEEE!

WHACK!

THERE—THAT'S TWO SACKS OF SOOT LOADED ON MY CART!

SOOT

SOOT

SWEEP

Suddenly—

EH?

HELP!

A huge cloud of soot rises over Doggie Patch—

WHUMF!

WHOOSH!

SWEEP

So—

HEY, DAWG! MY WINDOWS ARE ALL SOOTY! GIVE THEM A CLEAN!

MINE TOO!

MY WINDOWS NEXT, DAWG!

I'M DOING A BRISK BUSINESS NOW, SHERIFF! I LIKE YOUR NEW OUTFIT! WOULD YOU LIKE IT SHINED?

CLANK! CLANK!

THE BURRD'S BUDDIES

The RED SPARROWS

JONATHAN SWIFT

MAGGIE PIE

STARLING MOSS

VROOM!

ROLLO

EVERYONE in dockland knew Rollo Robson, because Rollo was the neighbourhood's ace roller-skater! He could be seen almost any day, heading for the local roller-rink, which was housed in a specially-converted dockside warehouse.

Little did Rollo realise, as he jogged along the quayside one morning, that his roller-skating skills were about to lead to an exciting adventure.

I CAN'T WAIT TO START SKATING TODAY!

But suddenly—

OH, NO! MY SKATES!

THE BAG'S SINKING FAST! I WON'T REACH IT IN TIME!

GASP! WHAT'S HAPPENING?

Rollo was only too happy to oblige!

GREAT STUFF, ROLLO! KEEP PRACTISING AND YOU'LL BE A CHAMPION ONE DAY!

THANKS, BERT! NOW I'D BETTER HEAD HOME FOR LUNCH!

As Rollo made his way back along the dockside . . .

HEY, RICKY! ARE YOU STILL BUSY?

SHOVE OFF, KID! AND MIND YOUR OWN BUSINESS!

ULP! HE'S NOT RICKY!

But Rollo only went as far as the next corner.

WHAT'S GOING ON? THAT GUY'S WEARING RICKY'S WET-SUIT AND THAT LOOKED LIKE A GOLD GOBLET HE WAS PULLING OUT OF THE WATER!

Just then, something at a warehouse door, glinted in the sun.

WHAT'S THAT DOWN THERE?

A DIVER'S WATCH! AND I'M SURE IT'S THE ONE RICKY WAS WEARING EARLIER TODAY!

Rollo decided to see what was INSIDE that warehouse . . .

IT'S RICKY! THAT OTHER DIVER MUST HAVE TIED HIM UP, SO HE COULD STEAL THE TREASURE FROM THE SUNKEN GALLEON!

But before the young skater could help his friend the sound of footsteps sent Rollo running.

SO, THERE'S MORE THAN ONE CROOK! I'D BETTER HIDE!

WE SHOULD HAVE ALL THE GOLD UP FROM THE WRECK BY THIS AFTERNOON! . . .

. . . THEN ALL WE'LL HAVE TO DO IS GET RID OF THAT DIVER!

THE BOSS WILL BE PLEASED!

RICKY'S IN DANGER! I'VE GOT TO MOVE FAST!

And the fastest way to move was on roller-skates!

HEY!

EXCUSE ME, FOLKS! THIS IS AN EMERGENCY!

Rollo gathered speed as he weaved in and out of the dockland sheds and warehouses but when he reached the swing bridge . . .

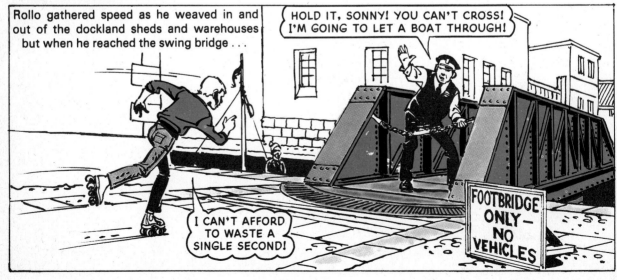

HOLD IT, SONNY! YOU CAN'T CROSS! I'M GOING TO LET A BOAT THROUGH!

I CAN'T AFFORD TO WASTE A SINGLE SECOND!

FOOTBRIDGE ONLY — NO VEHICLES

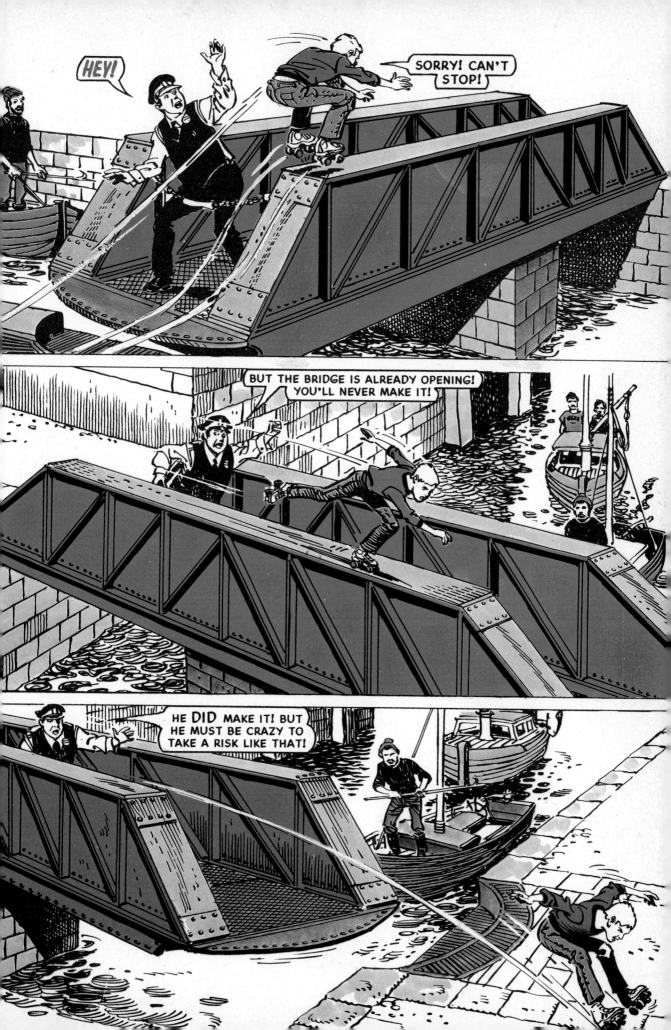

And soon, Rollo was speeding towards his destination.

COME QUICKLY! THERE'S A DIVER IN TROUBLE DOWN AT THE DOCKS!

GET INTO THAT PATROL CAR, LAD, AND SHOW US THE EXACT SPOT!

As the police roared towards the harbour, the crooked diver climbed from the water after another plundering expedition to the wreck.

And moments later, on the quayside—

HOLD IT RIGHT THERE! YOU'RE UNDER ARREST!

THE COPS!

The police had told Rollo to stay at a safe distance, but now it looked as if the law needed his help!

A HOODED GUNMAN! AND THE POLICEMEN HAVEN'T SEEN HIM!

BULLY BEEF AND CHIPS

MICKY the MOUTH

THE BOY WITH THE LOUDEST VOICE IN THE WORLD

I'D BETTER START PREPARING THE TEA!

WAIT! FOR A CHANGE, LET'S GO OUT FOR TEA! NO WASHING-UP AFTER WE'VE EATEN!

GOOD IDEA!

So—

WE'LL GO IN HERE!

YUM-YUM!

THERE WE ARE, MADAM!

THANKS, MATE!

EEK!

OOF!

LEAP

CRASH!

SSSH! KEEP QUIET, MICKY!

I WAS ONLY TRYING TO BE POLITE!

WE'RE READY TO ORDER NOW!

OH...I SAY, WAITER!

HMM! THE WAITER WON'T HEAR DAD!

Shortly—

Then—

JACK SILVER

I**S it a bird? Is it a dog? Or is it something in between? And why is this weird creature towing Earth boy, Curly Perkins, and his space pal, Jack Silver, over the mysterious mountains of far off Planet Marsuvia?**

The answers to these questions are in the amazing adventure which begins over the page.

Curly Perkins could never have imagined all the strange things which were about to happen when he visited Marsuvia to go bird-watching with his pal, Jack Silver.

WE'LL SEE SOME UNUSUAL BIRDS OVER ON ZARRAN ISLAND, CURLY! THERE'S A BRIDGE NEARBY WHERE WE CAN CROSS.

But then—

OH, NO! THE BRIDGE HAS RUSTED AWAY! WE CAN'T VISIT THE ISLAND NOW!

LOOK OVER THERE, JACK! SOMEONE SEEMS TO HAVE ORGANISED FLIGHTS OVER TO THE ISLAND!

But when the boys reached the shuttle-craft, they saw a very familiar face.

CAPTAIN ZAPP! HE'S IN CHARGE OF THE FLIGHTS TO THE ISLAND! WHAT'S THAT CROOK UP TO?

FARES PLEASE! CHUCKLE!

ZAPP-AIR
FLIGHTS TO ISLAND— FARE – 20 ZOUNDS

HE'S CHARGING PEOPLE A FORTUNE FOR THAT SHORT FLIGHT BECAUSE THEY CAN'T USE THE BRIDGE!

WELL WE'RE NOT PAYING ZAPP TO TAKE US ACROSS! IF WE FOLLOW THIS TRAIL OF BONES I'M SURE WE'LL FIND A SWOOPHOUND! IT CAN FLY US TO THE ISLAND!

When he'd recovered, Jack led the Swoophound to an abandoned stage-copter the boys had spotted by the bridge.

THE STAGE-COPTER'S ROCKETS ARE OUT OF ACTION, SO WE'LL USE WING-POWER INSTEAD!

I'LL FIX ON HIS HARNESS, JACK!

Soon the boys were flying passengers across to the island, and there was no shortage of customers, for the boys' flight was FREE! Everyone was happy . . . except Captain Zapp!

ZAH! THOSE BRATS ARE STEALING MY CUSTOMERS! I'LL PUT A STOP TO THIS!

Zapp pulled on his ship's control column and swung into the attack.

With his laser cannons
blasting, the villain swooped
down on the boys.

Jack knew exactly what to do!

ZAPP WON'T FIND IT SO EASY TO FOLLOW US WHEN HE CAN'T SEE WHERE HE'S GOING!

ZAH! MY WINDSCREEN'S COVERED IN INK!

NOW LET'S GET OUT OF HERE! ...COME ON, BOY, TAKE US UP INTO THE CLOUDS!

CAPTAIN ZAPP WILL HAVE TROUBLE CHASING US IN THIS THICK CLOUD.

Peering through the ink-spattered glass, Zapp was still determined to catch the boys.

THOSE BRATS WON'T GIVE ME THE SLIP!

ZULP! I DIDN'T REALISE THIS CLOUD WAS SO THICK! I CAN'T SEE A THING!

THE BURRD

YEAH! YEAH!

LET'S SEE WHO CAN GET THE MOST AUTOGRAPHS AT THE SHOW-JUMPING, BURRD!

YEAH! YEAH!

I'LL TRY FOR MY FIRST AUTOGRAPH HERE.

ZOOM!

HARVEY BLACKSMITH

EH?

YOO-HOO! SIGN, PLEASE!

AARGH!

WHIZZ!

STOP

SCREEECH!

I'M NOT JUMPING OVER THAT FEATHER-BRAIN!

CRASH!

OOF!

PEST!

ULP!

NOW FOR BASIL BROOME'S AUTOGRAPH!

BOUNCE-!

BOB!

SIGN, PLEASE!

YIKE!

But there IS someone looking after the frogs—WATCHFROG!

I'LL GUARD THE BANK WHILE BRETT BADGER IS AWAY!

LITTLE RIVER BANK

YOU'LL NEED SOME GRUB WHILE YOU'RE ON DUTY, WATCHFROG!

STRETCH!

THANKS, TOADY!

GLUB!

WHACK

HA-HA!

HEH-HEH! HE CAN'T RAISE THE ALARM NOW—HE'S GOT A FROG IN HIS THROAT!

YUM-YUM! TWO LADY FROGS TOO BUSY CHATTING TO SPOT ME

GOSSIP!

GOSSIP!

HERE GOES!

EEK! THEY'RE STANDING ON A WATER LILY!

HEE-HEE! THERE'S CLAWS MAKING A SPLASH ABOUT SOMETHING!

SPLOSH!

TUESDAY—
MENDED A PUNCTURE IN MY BIKE — THE EASY WAY!

COME BACK WITH MY WHEEL, YOU ROTTER!

WEDNESDAY—
CHIPS WENT JOGGING — AND I WENT JAGGING!

HELP!

SATURDAY—
ENJOYED A WEEK-END TRIP!

TRIP

OOF!

SUNDAY—
AHEM — A DAY OF REST!

HO-HO! SILLY BEEFY WROTE DOWN ALL HE DID—AND HIS DAD FOUND THE DIARY!

OOYAH!

TOM TUM

BRR! I'M COLD— AND HUNGRY!

Then— SLURP!

BUZZ OFF!

THROW!

SPLAT!

OW!

BRR! NOW I'M COLDER —AND HUNGRIER THAN EVER!

SHAKE!

SOUP

MAYBE I'LL GET SOMETHING IN HERE!

CLEAR OFF!

OH, DEAR! SPOTTED AGAIN!

EXCUSE ME! YOU'RE JUST THE BOY I'M LOOKING FOR. I'LL GIVE YOU AS MUCH GRUB AS YOU CAN SCOFF!

GREAT!

I'LL HAVE SOME SOUP, AND HOT CROSS BUNS AND—

NO, NO! THIS IS WHAT YOU'LL BE EATING!

ICE CREAM?

BUY WOOLLO COATS—THEY'LL KEEP YOU WARM WHILE EATING ICE CREAM!

MUST BE WARM!

I'LL HAVE ONE!

HEE-HEE! I'M NOT COLD ANY MORE, BUT I'M STILL PECKISH—MORE ICE CREAM, PLEASE!

THAT'S THE DINGHY DEFLATED—TO OUR HUT NOW, LADS!

I'LL DRY MY DAMP SHOES ON THIS UGLY MAT.

Presently—

WE'VE FOLLOWED THE GEORDIES TO THEIR HUT. YOU KNOW WHAT TO DO, WEE ECK?

AYE.

OKAY, JOCKS! BOMBARD THIS SIDE OF THE HUT, WHILE ECK SNEAKS ROUND THE BACK!

BONK!

THUMP!

Inside—

COME ON, MATEYS, TO THE WINDOW WITH YOUR CATTIES! WE'LL RETURN THE BROADSIDE!

PULL TO INFLATE

Meanwhile—

THEY'RE TOO BUSY TO NOTICE ME. EASY DOES IT...

Down below—

NEARLY THERE!

PULL TO INFLATE

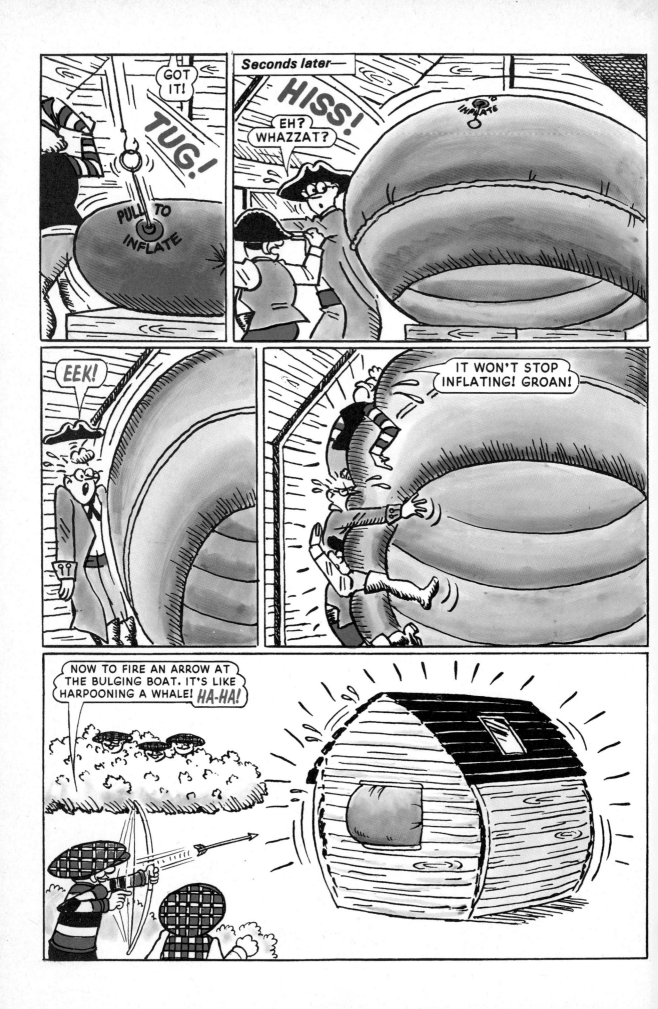

But the rib-tickling tale started earlier that day when Winker was with his pal, Tim Trott . . .

TOSS!

I COULD EAT A HORSE, TIM, BUT I'D RATHER EAT A BAG OF SWEETS!

GIVE ME A GIANT BAG OF TOFFEES, MR JENKINS!

Mr Jenkins was the school janitor, but it wasn't him that popped up.

GULP!

MR CREEP!

SCOOP!

GREYTOWERS PAINTING FUND!

SO KIND OF YOU TO DONATE THIS CASH! I HAVE TO RAISE £200 TO HAVE AN OIL PAINTING DONE OF OUR BELOVED SCHOOL!

ROTTEN OLD CREEPY! WE DIDN'T GET ANY SWEETS BECAUSE OF SOME SILLY PAINTING!

WHAT'S CHUBBY LOOKING AT?

GULP! I DON'T LIKE THE LOOK OF THAT!

Chubby Slowbottom was Greytowers School's worst sportsman, and Winker and Tim were keen to see what had upset him.

SO THIS IS CREEPY'S LATEST SCHEME! WELL, I'LL FIX HIM!

SPONSORED RUN TO RAISE FUNDS FOR SCHOOL PAINTING. ONE BOY WILL RUN. EVERY PUPIL MUST SPONSOR HIM

Later in class—

TOSS!

I'VE WRITTEN EACH BOY'S NAME ON A PIECE OF PAPER! THE NAME I DRAW OUT WILL BE THE BOY WHO GOES ON THE RUN! EVERY PUPIL WILL SPONSOR HIM FOR FIVE PENCE PER MILE!

I'VE A TOP HAT HERE, SIR! IT WOULD BE MORE FUN TO DRAW THE NAME OUT OF THAT!

AN EXCELLENT IDEA, WATSON! COME OUT AND TRANSFER THE NAMES!

NOW, BOYS, GET YOUR MONEY OUT!

TIP!

I'VE PUT MY OWN SET OF NAMES IN THE HAT! I CAN GET RID OF CREEPY'S!

WASTE PAPER

AND THE BOY WHO WILL RUN IS...CHUBBY SLOWBOTTOM!

PSST! EVERY NAME IN THE HAT WAS CHUBBY'S!

GULP!

Shortly—

YOUR MONEY'S SAFE, WINKER! I WON'T BE ABLE TO RUN FAR!

RATTLE!

RATTLE!

THAT WAS WHAT I PLANNED, CHUBBY!

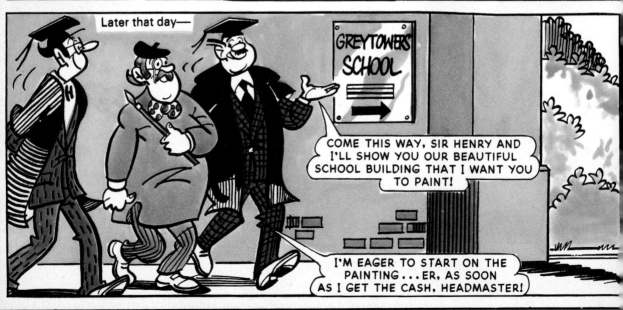

Sir Henry had no sooner set to work, when . . .

OH, NO! CREEPY'S GOING TO CLEAN UP THE SCHOOL BEFORE SIR HENRY'S FINISHED HIS PAINTING!

Winker tugged at the balloon's valve and next minute . . .

OOPS! SORRY, MR CREEP!

CRUMP!

URRFF!

Shortly—

I'VE FINISHED THE PAINTING! HERE'S SOMETHING FOR HELPING ME!

THANKS! I'LL SPEND IT AT THE FAIR!

Meanwhile—

SO, THERE YOU ARE, CREEP! I TOLD YOU TO CLEAN UP THE SCHOOL! GET UP AND START WORKING!

OOH!

And so—

CAN'T I USE SOMETHING BIGGER THAN A TOOTHBRUSH, HEADMASTER?

NO! YOU NEED A SMALL BRUSH TO GET INTO THE CRACKS AND CAVITIES!

WE'LL SEE YOU WHEN WE GET BACK FROM THE FAIR, MR CREEP!

DUMB BELLE

LET'S GO INTO THIS RAINWEAR SHOP. DAD SAID I HAD TO GET TOGGED OUT FOR A RAINY DAY!

CAN I HELP YOU?

A RAINCOAT, PLEASE!

HMM! THIS ONE'S TOO SMALL!

TUG

TUG

HO-HO! NO WONDER! BELLE IS WEARING IT ROUND THIS POLE.

PULL

FUNNY! IT SHOULD BE YOUR SIZE!

WELL—IT WOULDN'T FASTEN!

HEE-HEE!

BULLY BEEF and CHIPS in "MAD HATTERS"

WHAT'S IN THE BOX, CHIPS?

ONLY OLD HATS FOR THE JUMBLE SALE!

THIS MAKES ME LOOK LIKE A MAGICIAN!

AND FOR MY FIRST TRICK I SHALL PRODUCE SOME SWEETS!

HAW-HAW!

SNATCH!

AND NOW I'LL MAKE THEM DISAPPEAR—WATCH!

HUH!

THIS IS A NOVEL HAT!

WATCH CLOSELY!

EH?

IT'S A FOLDING TOP HAT! HA-HA!

OW!

THUD!

BASH!

BRASSNECK

GASPS of surprise turned to howls of horror as shrieking sun-bathers and terrified tourists scattered in panic. And the cause of all the trouble was a metal boy called Brassneck, and the creature he was taking for " walkies " along the beach — A HUGE, KILLER SHARK.

But our story starts at the home of the Brand family, on a freezing winter's day.

The Brands' house was deserted, but in the garden stood Mum, Dad, their son Charley and Charley's best pal, Brassneck . . . all made out of snow and built by the two boys.

The real Brands had decided to escape the winter weather by booking a holiday in the sun, and now their plane was about to touch down at a sunny Spanish airport.

And soon the Brands were in the airport waiting to collect their luggage.

THERE'S MY SUITCASE!

HERE COMES MY HOLDALL!

AND THERE'S BRASSNECK!

THAT ROTTEN HOLIDAY COURIER MADE ME RIDE IN THE PLANE'S HOLD WITH THE LUGGAGE!

HMPH! I DON'T WANT THAT TIN FREAK ON A HOLIDAY I'M IN CHARGE OF!

TAXIS

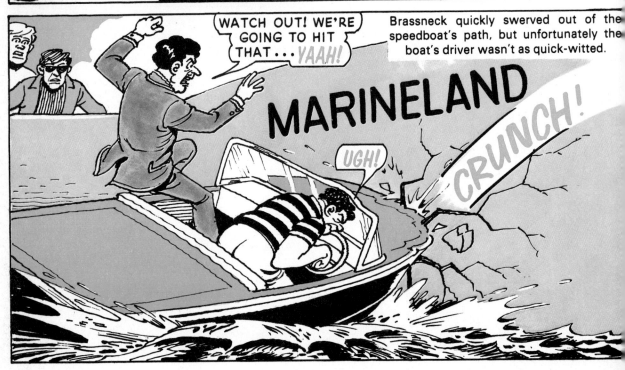

Marineland was an underwater zoo full of creatures from the deep, so when the wall shattered, more than water escaped through the huge gap.

The bathers scattered as the shark sped towards the beach.

And then . . .

I DON'T KNOW WHY EVERYONE WAS SO SCARED! I'VE BEEN HOLDING THIS OVER-SIZED FISH EVER SINCE IT ESCAPED! NOW I'LL TAKE IT BACK TO MARINELAND!

Charley and Brassneck met up with Mum and Dad again at a lively cafe.

THAT LADY IS A FLAMENCO DANCER! GOOD, ISN'T SHE?

HUH! I COULD DO THAT!

OLÉ!

WATCH **ME** DANCE ON THE TABLE!

STOP! BRASSNECK...

ULP! THE TABLE'S COLLAPSED! MUST HAVE HAD WOODWORM!

CRASH!

I'LL TRY THIS TABLE! MAYBE IT'S STRONGER!

OH, NO!

But Brassneck had soon tried dancing on EVERY table in the cafe and not one had been strong enough to take his weight.

YOU VANDALS!

THE OWNER'S NOT TOO PLEASED, BRASSNECK!

Seconds later, Dad Brand discovered just how displeased the cafe owner was.

NEVER COME BACK!

OUCH!

BOOT!

Back at the hotel—

IT'S TIME FOR LUNCH AND YOU'D BETTER BEHAVE, BRASSNECK!

IT'S THEM AGAIN.

I'LL HAVE SCAMPI AND CHIPS, WAITER!

PAELLA AND CHIPS, PLEASE!

I'LL HAVE OCTOPUS AND CHIPS!

MENU

BRING ME A CAN OF YOUR BEST MULTIGRADE MOTOR OIL AND SOME METAL ROAD CHIPS!

But the scheming courier also had a word with the waiter.

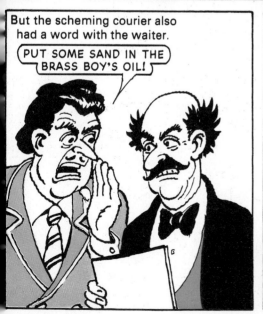

PUT SOME SAND IN THE BRASS BOY'S OIL!

MY OIL'S ARRIVED, AND THE CAN'S BEEN OPENED FOR ME. HOW KIND!

OIL
X X X

When Brassneck took a sip of the oil, the courier was watching his every move.

YEUCH! THAT OIL TASTES GRITTY!

OIL

I SAW YOU PUTTING THAT OIL ON THE FLOOR! I'M THROWING YOU OUT OF THE HOTEL!

UH?

YIKE! THE OIL'S SLIPPY!

SKID

CAN'T STOP!

HEY!

GLUB!

The courier crashed down on to one of the hotel balconies. He was lucky to make a soft landing, but UNLUCKY that his fall was cushioned by the holiday company boss.

With no sneaky courier to bother him, Brassneck could enjoy the rest of his holiday. And he knew it was now safe to tell everyone back home about the great time he was having.

DESPERATE DAWG

I'LL DO A SPOT OF HUNTING FROM MY LOG CABIN IN THE HILLS. I'D BETTER MAKE SURE I'VE BROUGHT MY KEY WITH ME.

OOPS! DROPPED IT IN THE SNOW!

PLOP!

HOI! GET OUT OF THE WAY!

AHA! HERE IT IS!

EH?

BUMP!

GLUMFF!

NOW LOOK WHAT YOU'VE DONE! YOU'VE BUSTED OUR SLEDGE!

IT HAS ONLY COME APART! IF I BANG IN THE NAILS, IT WILL BE ALL RIGHT AGAIN!

So—

BANG! BASH!

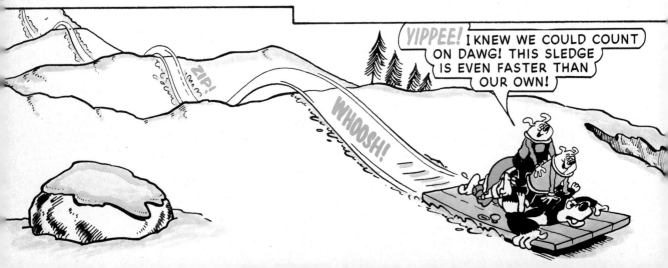

"HIPPO" DROME

FAMOUS GEORDIES